Learn to Sight Read

& HEAR THE DIFFERENCE

~ *A Unique Multi-Media Approach to Sight Reading* ~

by Sandy Holland & Peter Noke

First published in 2017 by E-MusicMaestroPublishing

E-MusicMaestroPublishing is a trading name of E-MusicMaestroPublishing Limited, Wallace Lane, Forton, Lancashire, PR30BB, UK

Design & Illustration by KevAdamson.com Ltd

*Printed in England by Halstan & Co Limited
Amersham, Buckinghamshire, UK*

TO THE TEACHER

Just another sight reading book? No! It's a new take on the age-old tradition of learning to speak a language - in this case the language of music - with fluency, from the outset. The authors are seasoned teachers and highly experienced examiners who apply current modes of learning to the best pedagogical principles.

Free QR code technology means that your student can listen to each piece first, play it and then listen again. Listening before playing helps with musical syntax and character. Listening after playing helps with self-assessing the accuracy. Your students will discover that having help at hand whilst practising at home means they can progress more quickly. Success breeds success, so students find this approach much more engaging.

HOW TO USE THE QR CODES

Please download the free Norton Snap QR code reader to your mobile phone or tablet by going to iTunes, Google Play or Android Market Place. Once your reader is installed simply open the app and point it at the QR code at the end of each piece for instant access to the performances!

The pieces are tuneful, with fun titles that mirror the rhythms of the first few bars. Several are based on known tunes, for extra motivation. **The content covers every rhythm pattern, metre and note range that may be encountered in any piano exam at this level.** At the end of each set, your student can take a sight reading test in real time, online. All examples are also available online as timed sight reading tests at *www.e-musicmaestro.com*.

Teachers can keep in touch with us online at *www.e-musicmaestro.com* where you'll find great, free teaching tips. All you need to make the best use of this book is a mobile phone or tablet and an internet connection. However, if you prefer not to use a multimedia approach, you can use the book in the traditional way.

TO THE PUPIL

You're going to love this book because the pieces have good tunes! Try saying the title of each piece out loud before you play it and notice how the words sound just like the rhythm of the first phrase.

Before you begin, you need to set up the free QR code app on your phone or tablet. The instructions are on the page opposite.

Using the QR code app, listen to a piece then have a go at playing it, as many times as you like. Listen again to the recording and learn by comparing it with how you played. Then move onto the next piece.

Play a piece every day and, by the time you've finished the book, you should be fluent at sight reading at this grade, ready to get a good mark in your exam.

You can practise for your exam by going to the last page of each set where you'll find a special test piece which you can do in real time, just like it will be in the exam.

In this book you will find pieces in these keys:
C major D major
F major G major
D minor A minor

We've mixed them up for you, so that you can practise going from one key to another.

You'll also see top tips from me – Maestro the Dog!

My Progress Chart

Tick boxes when you complete each item

No. 1		No. 6	
No. 2		No. 7	
No. 3		No. 8	
No. 4		No. 9	
No. 5		No. 10	

I finished Set 1 on this date: _____ / _____ / _____ .

Completed the Set?
Give yourself a
pat on the back!

Playfully   *Answer My Question, Truthfully!*

Grandly   *I've Got a Big Red Ball!*

Happily   *Let's All Go to Mexico*

Now try a Sight Reading Test!

Use this QR code to take you to a timed test under 'exam conditions' :

My Progress Chart

SET 2

Tick boxes when you complete each item

No. 1		No. 6	
No. 2		No. 7	
No. 3		No. 8	
No. 4		No. 9	
No. 5		No. 10	

I finished Set 2 on this date: _____ / _____ / _____ .

Allegretto

Late Today

Smoothly

Blue Sea and Sun and Sand

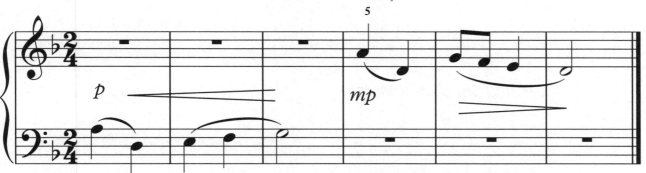

Gently

Time to Go to Sleep

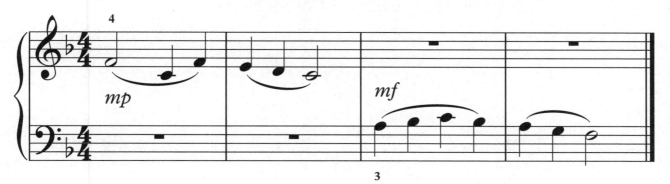

Now try a Sight Reading Test!

Use this QR code to take you to a timed test under 'exam conditions' :

My Progress Chart

SET 3

Tick boxes when you complete each item

No. 1		No. 6		
No. 2		No. 7		
No. 3		No. 8		
No. 4		No. 9		
No. 5		No. 10		

I finished Set 3 on this date: _____ / _____ / _____ .

Completed the Set?
Give yourself
a nice treat!

Andante

Creeping up Behind You

Allegretto

Running Down, Running Up

Allegretto

When Will We Meet Again?

Now try a Sight Reading Test!

Use this QR code to take you to a timed test under 'exam conditions' :

My Progress Chart

SET 4

Tick boxes when you complete each item

No. 1		No. 6	
No. 2		No. 7	
No. 3		No. 8	
No. 4		No. 9	
No. 5		No. 10	

I finished Set 4 on this date: _____ / _____ / _____ .

Completed the Set?
Hot Diggety Dog!

Wobbling along

Red Jelly and Ice Cream

Bouncy

Raining Cats and Dogs Today

Strictly in time

Marching Tune

Now try a Sight Reading Test!

Use this QR code to take you to a timed test under 'exam conditions' :

My Progress Chart

Tick boxes when you complete each item

No. 1		No. 6	
No. 2		No. 7	
No. 3		No. 8	
No. 4		No. 9	
No. 5		No. 10	

I finished Set 5 on this date: _____ / _____ / _____ .

Gently

Little Brown Hen

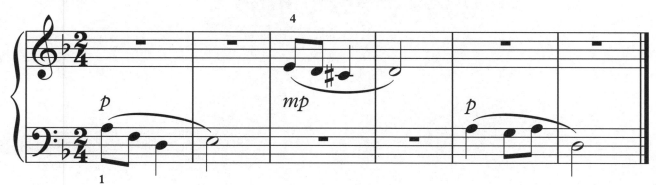

Andante

Put Your Umbrella Up – It Looks Like Rain

Allegretto

Hopping Up, Running Down

Now try a Sight Reading Test!

Use this QR code to take you to a timed test under 'exam conditions' :

My Progress Chart

Tick boxes when you complete each item

No. 1		No. 6	
No. 2		No. 7	
No. 3		No. 8	
No. 4		No. 9	
No. 5		No. 10	

I finished Set 6 on this date: _____ / _____ / _____ .

Completed the Set?
Congratulations!

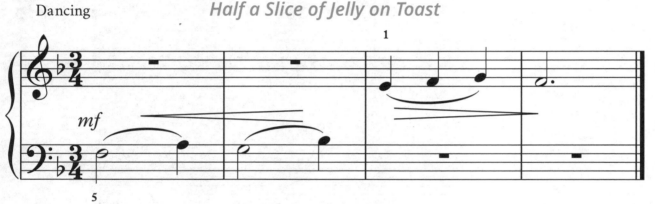

Smoothly

Rolling Down a Hill

Andante

Wouldn't You Like to Know?

Smoothly

Watching the Boats Go By

Now try a Sight Reading Test!

Use this QR code to take you to a timed test under 'exam conditions' :

My Progress Chart

SET 7

Tick boxes when you complete each item

No. 1		No. 6	
No. 2		No. 7	
No. 3		No. 8	
No. 4		No. 9	
No. 5		No. 10	

I finished Set 7 on this date: _____ / _____ / _____ .

Completed the Set? I'll be Doggoned!

Slowly

Three Sad Mice

Merrily

Merrily We Play our Scales

Slowly

Sammy the Curly Wurly Snail

Now try a Sight Reading Test!

Use this QR code to take you to a timed test under 'exam conditions' :

My Progress Chart

SET 8

Tick boxes when you complete each item

No. 1		No. 6	
No. 2		No. 7	
No. 3		No. 8	
No. 4		No. 9	
No. 5		No. 10	

I finished Set 8 on this date: _____ / _____ / _____ .

Completed the Set?
Whoopee!

Gliding Down, Walking Up

Oh No! What Have You Done!

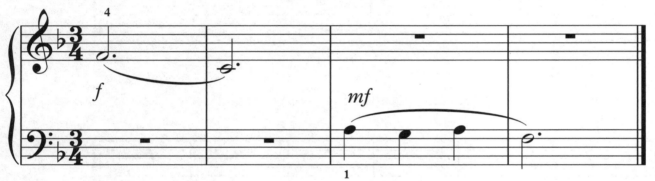

Creeping Up Quietly...BOO!

Andante

Walking on a Sunny Day

Bouncy

Pitter Patter

Allegretto

Coffee or Tea? Tea for Me!

Now try a Sight Reading Test!

Use this QR code to take you to a timed test under 'exam conditions' :

My Progress Chart

SET 9

Tick boxes when you complete each item

No. 1		No. 6	
No. 2		No. 7	
No. 3		No. 8	
No. 4		No. 9	
No. 5		No. 10	

I finished Set 9 on this date: _____ / _____ / _____ .

Completed the Set?
Awesome!

Lively

Jumping and Prancing

Grandly

Big Procession

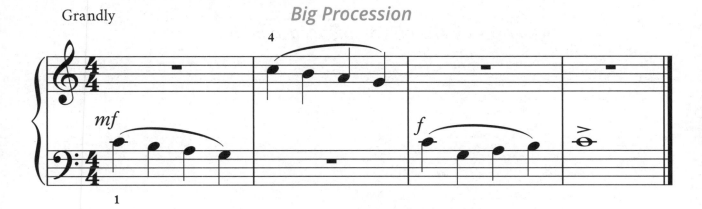

Gently

Falling Asleep

Now try a Sight Reading Test!

Use this QR code to take you to a timed test under 'exam conditions' :

My Progress Chart

SET 10

Tick boxes when you complete each item

No. 1		No. 6	
No. 2		No. 7	
No. 3		No. 8	
No. 4		No. 9	
No. 5		No. 10	

I finished Set 10 on this date: _____ / _____ / _____ .

Completed the Set?
Celebrate!

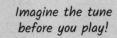

Andante · **Walking Through the Wood**

Spookily · **Ghosts and Skeletons**

Moderato · **Now It's Your Turn!**

42

Lively   *Leaping High*

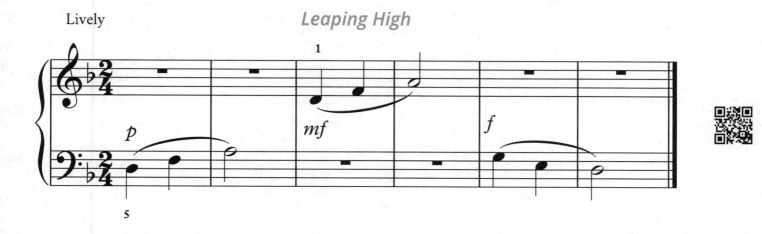

Smoothly   **Running Down the Hill**

Moderato   **Goodbye Until Book 2!**

Now try a Sight Reading Test!

Use this QR code to take you to a timed test under 'exam conditions' :